Uncle Pete the Pirate

Susannah Leigh

Illustrated by Brenda Haw

Edited by Louie Stowell

Cover design by Zoe Waring

Contents

Adventure ahoy!

Keep your eyes open for clues. If you get stuck, there are answers on pages 31 and 32.

MARY

UNCLE PETE

Mary's uncle Pete the pirate is coming to visit and she just can't wait. What exciting adventures will he have in store for her?

Uncle Pete arrives

Mary raced down to the little port near her house, feeling fizzy with excitement. She had promised to meet Uncle Pete there, but she couldn't see him. "I wonder if he's wearing his pirate hat?" she thought. "That'll make him easier to spot."

Where's Uncle Pete?

Funfair Today

5

Wonderful presents

Mary saw Uncle Pete and rushed over to him. "Ahoy there!" she called, in her best pirate voice.

Pete chuckled. "I have a surprise for you," he said and laid out some wonderful presents on the table. "Where'd you think I found these?"

6

"Give me a clue?" said Mary. She didn't say please, because pirates don't expect you to be polite.

"I will," said Pete, and he started to tell her about his pirate adventures in faraway places. Mary soon worked out where all her presents came from.

Where did they come from?

The piratey house

"You might get bored," Mary sighed, as they walked to her house. "Nothing piratey ever happens here."

"Nonsense, your house is a pirate's playground!" Uncle Pete replied.

"Look more closely," Pete added.
Mary blinked. Yes, he was right! Today
her house looked very piratey indeed.

Can you spot any pirate things at Mary's house?

9

A mysterious message

Mary had a feeling a pirate adventure was just around the corner. Sure enough, when they got inside, Uncle Pete handed her a postcard. "I found this on the doorstep."

"It seems to be a message of some kind," said Mary.

What does the card say?

Dear Mary
go to this 🧰
and find a 📜
from a well-wisher ☠

The treasure map

Avast ye, pirates young and old
Here be a map to pirate gold
A picture of Bad Luck Barry
Marks the spot
The treasure isn't
where Barry is not.

Saucepan Island

School House

Aunty Brenda's House

Sand castle Island

Puppy Island

"Shivering Shipwrecks!" cried Uncle Pete, as they opened the chest and pulled out a scroll of paper. "It's a treasure map!"

"Orrible octupuses!" Mary exclaimed, feeling very piratey.

She took the map and eagerly
read the poem at the top. A few
seconds later she cried, "I can see where
the treasure is!"

Where did Barry bury the treasure?

13

Uncle Pete explains

"There," said Mary. She pointed
to the picture of Bad
Luck Barry burying the
treasure. "But who is he?"
Uncle Pete sighed. "He's my oldest
pirate enemy...

He stole my
precious treasure...

...and hid it on
Lawnmower
Island.
We should watch out
for him. He's probably
somewhere near!"

Mary felt scared,
but excited too. "I wonder where
he is?" she thought.

Can you see Barry?

15

The pirate boat

"When he realizes his map's gone, he'll be hopping mad!" said Pete. "We need to sail to Lawnmower Island right away."

"We need something to sail in first," said Mary.

So they scrambled up to the roof to have a look around. "I can see a boat that would do," Mary cried.

Can you see a boat they can use?

17

Puzzling parrots

Mary and Uncle Pete
set sail.

They passed
curious cows who
asked, "Moo are you?"
and pretty shiny fish
who flew.

Ahoy, landlubbers!

Further on,
two pirate parrots
squawked out a rhyme.

Pieces of eight, pieces of eight!
You must follow the arrows
They'll take you straight
to Barry's treasure
but haven't you seen?
They've been pointing the way
all along the stream.

Mary looked back down the river.
"By Long John Silver's only leg!" she
exclaimed. "There they are!"

Can you spot all the arrows?

19

Juicy jellyfish

"Lawnmower Island, dead ahead!" cried
Uncle Pete, "I'll tie up the boat."

Mary jumped out and splashed through
the shallow water. She quickly spotted a
blue arrow, pointing them to the right
path. She'd almost reached the island's soft
warm sand when a shout from
Uncle Pete stopped her.

"The beach is covered in juicy yellow jellyfish," he warned. "They could give you a nasty sting, even with your boots on!"

Mary looked down and saw one. "You won't sting me, Mr. Jellyfish!" she cried. She hopped over it and looked around for the others.

Can you find all the jellyfish?

21

Wild beast!

Mary and Pete followed the blue
arrow that pointed the way into the
dark and tangled jungle, closer to
Uncle Pete's treasure... until a loud
roar stopped them in their tracks.

Mary turned around, trembling.
She was face to face with a
large, hairy beast with very
sharp teeth.

"It's the wild beast of Lawnmower Island," Pete hissed. "If we can give it some tasty bones, we'll be able to sneak past safely."

Can you find seven bones for the wild beast to munch?

23

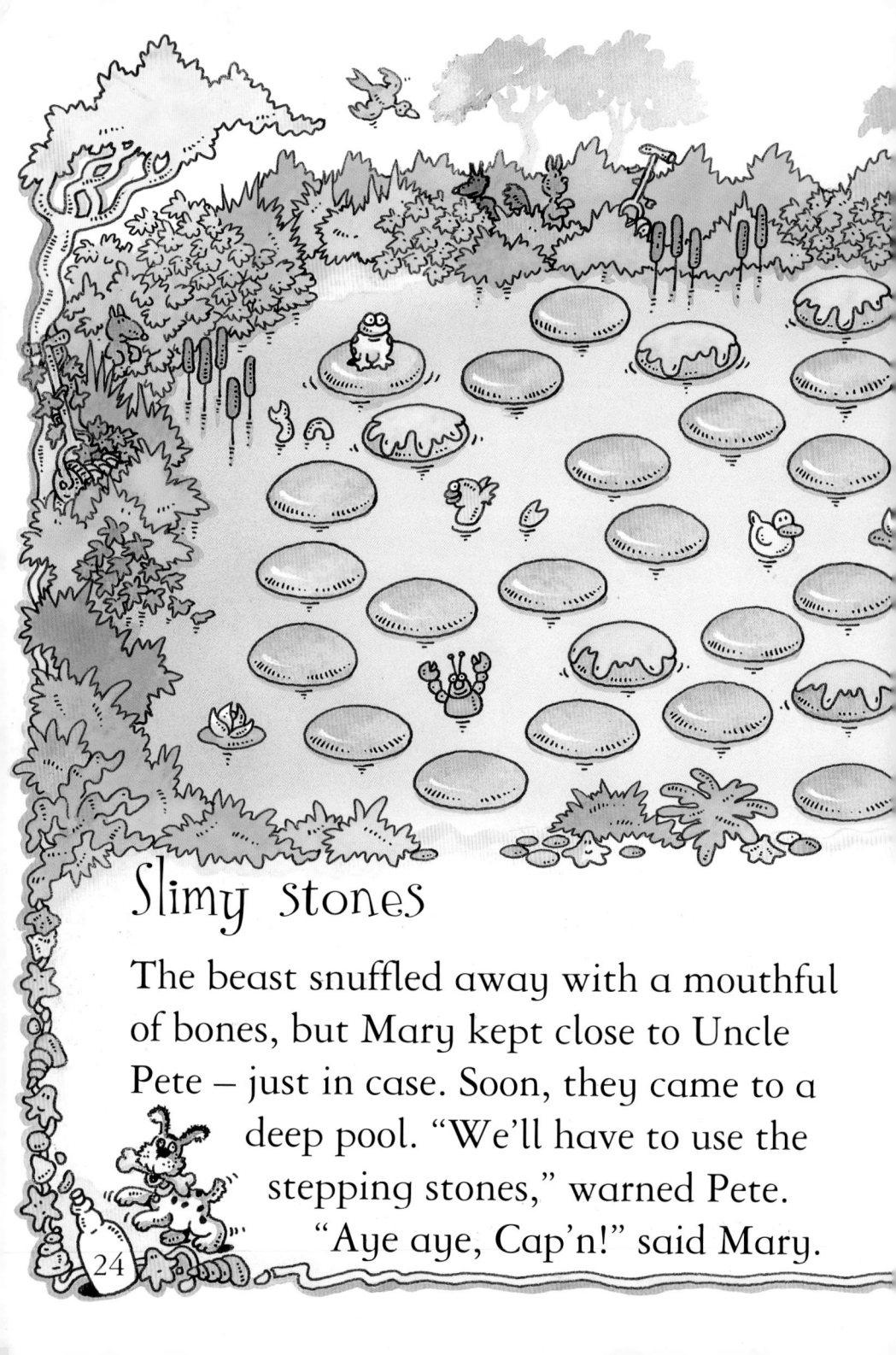

Slimy stones

The beast snuffled away with a mouthful
of bones, but Mary kept close to Uncle
Pete – just in case. Soon, they came to a
deep pool. "We'll have to use the
stepping stones," warned Pete.
"Aye aye, Cap'n!" said Mary.

She jumped onto a stone nearby, then the next one and the next. She was careful to avoid the slippery slime and the fat croaking toads.

Can you find a safe way across the stones to the blue arrow on the other side?

Pirate treasure

As Mary bounded onto dry land, she gasped. There sat the last people she was expecting – her parents!

Her mother smiled. "I have a feeling you'll find something buried just over there," she said, handing Mary a shovel.

So Mary started to dig. Thud! The blade of the shovel hit something hard. It was Uncle Pete's treasure chest.

But instead of treasure, Mary found a delicious pirate picnic inside. She grinned. "You planned this all along!" she said to her parents and Uncle Pete.

Then she had a terrifying thought. "What if Bad Luck Barry comes after the chest?" she said in a trembly voice.

Uncle Pete pointed to his evil pirate enemy and Mary laughed with relief.

Why isn't Mary scared of Barry?

Peteless

"So, he was only a scarecrow all along!" said Mary, feeling silly.

Then they all sailed back to town. As they strolled happily through the fair, Mary noticed that Uncle Pete was missing.

Where has Uncle Pete gone?

GHOST TRAIN

BUGG

Have Fun!

FUNFAIR

TODAY ONLY!

BALLS AND FLUTES — PRIZE EVER TIME

Funfair

"Climb aboard," called Uncle Pete.

Mary scrambled up onto the ride and clung on tight. "This has been the best pirate adventure ever," she cried.

"Just wait until my next visit," said Pete, with a wink.

Answers

Uncle Pete has one more puzzle for you. How many lawn mowers can you find on Lawnmower Island?

Pages 4-5

Uncle Pete is here.

Pages 6-7

Here is where Uncle Pete found each of Mary's presents. The octopus gave him the flute and the king gave him the cup. The brush belonged to the mermaid and the monkey threw Uncle Pete a coconut. Neptune gave Uncle Pete a listening shell, and the ball is the one the dolphins are playing with.

Pages 8-9

The pirate things at Mary's house are circled in this picture.

Pages 10-11

The card tells Mary to go to this chest

and find this map. Did you spot the note from Mary's parents? It says: Dear Mary, Gone fishing. Uncle Pete will look after you. Love Ma and Pa.

Pages 12-13

The treasure is buried on Lawnmower Island. Here is Bad Luck Barry hiding it.

Pages 14-15

Barry is here.

Pages 16-17

Mary has spotted a rubber dinghy which they can use as a pirate boat. Here it is.

Pages 18-19

The blue arrows have been pointing the right way to go. They are circled here.

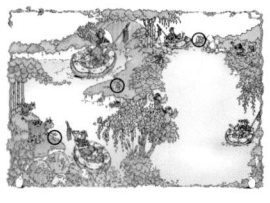

Pages 20-21

You can see the eleven jellyfish that Mary has to watch out for circled here.

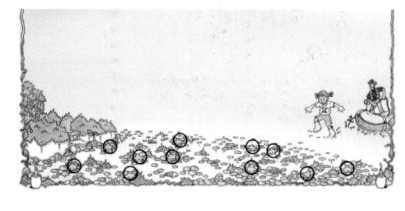

Pages 22-23

The seven juicy bones are circled here.

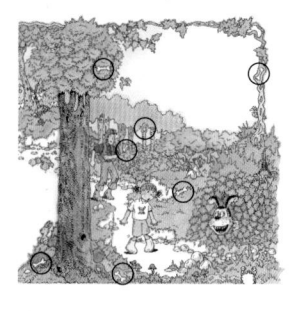

Pages 24-25

The way across the stepping stones to the blue arrow is marked in black.

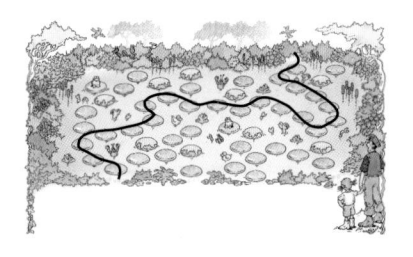

Pages 26-27

Bad Luck Barry won't want any treasure because he is really a scarecrow! Here he is.

(Did you spot him on page 17 being carried by the farmer?)

Pages 28-29

Uncle Pete is here. Did you guess?

(Can you see some familiar presents here?)

There are ten lawn mowers on Lawnmower Island.

This edition first published in 2007 by Usborne Publishing Ltd., Usborne House, 83-85 Saffron Hill, London EC1N 8RT, England. www.usborne.com Copyright © 2007, 2002, 1994 Usborne Publishing Ltd. The name Usborne and the devices ♡ 🜨 are Trade Marks of Usborne Publishing Ltd. All rights reserved.